AWAKENINGS

Stories and prayers
by
Hilary Faith Jones

with
foreword and illustrations
by
Eddie Askew

Published by The Leprosy Mission International

All rights and subsidiary rights have been granted to
The Leprosy Mission International
80 Windmill Road
Brentford
Middlesex TW8 0QH, United Kingdom
Please see page 88 for address and contact details.

Published in 1999
A catalogue record for this book is available from the British Library

ISBN 0 902731 41 6

Cover illustration: **MORNING LIGHT ON THE BAY**, watercolour
Illustration above: **THE PATHWAY**, pastel

For Mum and Dad
who put my hand in Christ's

EVENING LIGHT, YORKSHIRE COAST, *pastel*

Books of meditations, Bible readings and prayers by Eddie Askew,
published by The Leprosy Mission International:
A Silence and A Shouting   *Disguises of Love*
Many Voices One Voice   *No Strange Land*
Facing the Storm   *Breaking the Rules*
Cross Purposes   *Slower than Butterflies*
Music on the Wind

Other books published by The Leprosy Mission International:
The Song of the Sparrow by Alison Stedman
Awakenings by Hilary Faith Jones

Famous books by Paul Brand:
Ten Fingers for God   *Granny Brand*
The Gift of Pain   *Fearfully and Wonderfully Made*

All of the above books are available direct from:

TLM TRADING LIMITED
PO Box 212, Peterborough, PE2 5GD
Tel: 01733 239252, Fax: 01733 239258
E-mail: tlmtrading@dial.pipex.com

FOREWORD

Hilary has great insight and imagination. She lives in her stories and in the lives of the people she portrays. She searches their minds and hearts, identifies their feelings. Her words breathe new life into stories we know well – too well perhaps and taken for granted – and offers them to us with great economy of language.

She is a storyteller, part of an ancient tradition born before writing had begun. Many of them were women. Their presence in a community was welcomed warmly. They held history in their hands but shared it in a way that made every telling new. In imagination I see them blanket-wrapped in a cold courtyard, the day's work done, faces lit by fire glow as they listen under the stars. The storyteller takes the happening and makes it new, vibrant. The characters she clothes in contemporary dress and offers them to her listeners. And in the telling the story becomes relevant to the life they live.

This is what Hilary offers to us. She brings to life people who move through the pages of the Gospels and shares their humanity with us. We can feel with them, rejoice with them, doubt and fear with them. They are real.

Her meditations and the prayers that go with them are geared to the major festivals of the Christian year. Given the time they deserve they can spark the imagination into life. They take us below the surface, deep into human emotion, and challenge us to share the hopes and fears of those she writes about. Read them and reflect.

Eddie Askew

CONTENTS

Chapter One
ADVENT

THE VISITOR

God clapped a hand to his head.
I need an angel! he cried.
He looked around the heavens and glimpsed one swooping.
Gabriel! I've a job for you!
With a flutter of wings and flash of light,
Gabriel arrived in Mary's house.
Peace be with you, he said.
Mary was so startled
that she dropped the bread.
The Lord is with you and has greatly blessed you.
Mary,
a girl of spirit,
stood her ground firmly
but her eyes grew wide with fear.
For not only was Gabriel something of a shock but –
she didn't understand what he meant.

Gabriel was slightly put out.
Hey up Mary. Don't look so frightened.
God's pleased with you.
In fact, he's so pleased he's sending you a special baby.
You're going to call him Jesus.

Gabriel paused,
for, being an angel, he was utterly honest.
Actually, he's going to have lots of names –
Son of the most high,
King of Kings,
Messiah,
Counsellor,
Prince of Peace...
Gabriel gazed away with excitement and anticipation.

But Mary's eyes were aghast;
for she saw the shame for her parents,
herself cast out,
her betrothed humiliated,
disgrace on all whom she loved.
But how can this be? she whispered,
I am not married.

And Gabriel saw the tears roll down her cheeks
and forgot for a moment,
to be glorious
and ethereal.

Come Mary,
he said, and held her hand like another child.
God will enfold you in his love,
encircle the baby inside you,
and he will grow strong and true.

The girl Mary looked away
and saw the heartache
and the tears
and the joy
and the wonder.

Finally she spoke,
and her voice was strong
and vibrant,

Yes God! Yes!

When I believe
I have matured enough
When I believe
it's time that others were called
When I believe
that I have reached my full potential –

let me remember Lord
an ordinary girl
and how she flung wide her arms
to a windswept sky.

Help me Lord
to realise
that I've only just begun
my discipleship with you.

SUNNY DAY, *egg tempera*

THE KINSWOMAN

She stopped at the top of the rise,
shifted the heavy bags,
eased her straining arms.
She drank in the beauty of the land,
the promise of a new day.

Inside her,
the baby kicked determinedly,
beating tiny fists around his safety.
She sighed and laid her hand upon him,
soothing him with her voice,
caressing him with the murmuring of her thoughts.
She had the feeling
he'd come out kicking,
would live and die fighting,
this hot, tempestuous little life
that struggled within.

On reaching home she felt exhausted,
worn out by the heat and the closeness of the air.
She moved slowly,
putting the finishing touches of welcome,
ensuring all was clean and fresh and sweetly scented.

She finished
and lowered herself to the bed,
closing away the weariness,
the pain,
the tumult of the baby.

She'd always loved her husband,
loved him with straightforward honesty and determination.
And it was a good marriage,
held together by their faith and belief
in the goodness of God.

And because she loved him,
because of her strength of character,
she wanted to give him a child,
and then,
together they could marvel at creation,
together they could see delight grow,
together they could share the love, that came so easily to others.

Yet when, surprisingly, wondrously, it came,
it seemed fraught with so many difficulties,
so many unseen dangers.

And as the weeks turned into months,
she realised with dawning insight
how greatly she was loved –
saw it in the warmth of her friends,
in the pleasure of her family,
in the cherishing of her silent husband.

But in that loving she also saw his fear –
and in her soul she was afraid
for they both knew she was too old,
her body was not strong enough,
her heart was too frail,
her strength was not enough to carry another life within.

She woke with a start,
hearing the noise of arrival outside.
The sound of running feet
a laugh of delight,
the door flung open,
a shout of,
Elizabeth!
And her young, beautiful, radiant, cousin
was in her arms,
laughing, talking, exuberant, shining with life.

And at that moment
the baby leapt up with terrifying force,
hurtled joyously within,
seemed to reach out to embrace the vibrant girl.
Fire scorched through the weary body
power rushed into the frail heart.

And Elizabeth looked at the girl,
and saw for the first time
the loveliness and the beauty,
the strength and the courage,
and knew she looked at the woman of God.
And her work-worn hands
reached out and touched the girl
and her eyes filled with tears.
And for a moment,
all went still.

They did not need to speak
knowing that the spoken would
diminish and confine the glory of their journey.
Until, seeing the tears that would not stop,
the young girl took the older woman's hand
and kissed it gently,
gathered the tired soul into her arms,
tenderly cradled her;
took her exhaustion and pain,
her fear and her vulnerability;
and holding her,
she began to sing.

And the fears were shattered,
the weariness broken,
the tears cleansed,
faith restored
power infused
the kinswoman was lifted into strength.

And the tumultuous baby
felt the power of the loving,
felt the strength upholding;
breathed in the innocence,
and the wisdom,
of the song.

And so the one who was the messenger
and the one who is the way
grew strong and true,
wild and lovely;
strengthened by the fire, the vitality,
the fragility, the power, the glory
of the old and the young
who wove their dreams
upon the breath of God.

O my gentle God –

When my heart beats heavy
and I fear what lies ahead –
uncloud my soul
so that I may see you
in the loving that surrounds me.

When I am beyond my depth
and cannot understand the acts of youth
help me to stand still
within your pool of light
and simply be.

When I am oh, too tired
and I can fight no more –
take my hand I ask
and hold me close,
my gracious friend.

Hear the whispers in my heart
O my gentle, wondrous God.

TWILIGHT, NORFOLK, egg tempera

Chapter Two
CHRISTMAS

THE MEETING PLACE

The car spluttered, coughed, staggered into life again.
He heaved a sigh of relief and shot his passenger a quick
glance to see if she had noticed;
she had and was watching him, smiling.
He slowly grinned back and edged into the traffic.
Wickedly bad night for travelling.

They'd have been there hours ago if the car hadn't broken down –
twice.
As if reading his thoughts,
the car cut out,
and they drifted silently to the verge.

He clutched the wheel and felt sick.
I've no money left.
She looked at his tired face and forced a smile,
I'll get us a lift.
Before he could answer, she was gone – pushing through the rain,
holding his coat over her head, waving down a huge articulated
lorry.
He had to smile.
It was what had drawn him to her in the first place –
that rebellious spirit that would not be quelled.
When others had given up on her,
he'd kept on,
stuck by her.

People said he had a special way with her
but he didn't believe that.
It was just that she was different from the others,
had a spark of fire about her that came from –
well – somewhere different,
far removed from the ordinariness of life.

What he could not yet know
was that the more she was held down,
the greater her spirit grew.
The more she was pushed to conform,
the more she looked for the other.
For she had discovered that it was only the other who understood the
wild restlessness within her.
And to the gangly youth who grew into a man of stature,
who loved her steadily over the years,
it seemed that at times she shone,
as if she was the meeting place between earth and something beyond
his comprehension.

He sighed and pushed her up into the hot fugginess of the lorry cab,
let the driver ramble incessantly, watched her in growing anxiety.
She leant back in the corner, let her eyes close.
She'd always been one for trouble. She didn't seek it. It just found her.

Her mother warned her to keep quiet, keep her eyes down, to be like
other girls.
But despite what her mother said,
when the call came,
everything that was wild and most beautiful within her,
everything that was strong and courageous and passionate,
everything that belonged to a God who couldn't be conformed,
was set alight.
Of course I will,
she laughed in wonder to the star-brilliant heavens
and that night
she had danced with all her soul and all her delight.

She had told her parents of the child
with barely suppressed excitement.
Her feet still dancing
she had waited for their response,
holding her breath,
her eyes sparkling.
But they could not hear the truth in her.
Her mother sobbed silently and her father had suddenly looked old.
And cold reality had rushed in on the girl
and pain had stabbed through her heart.

Amazing how quickly the news spread.
Her friends giggled and whispered and were drawn away from her
by their mothers.
The boys made rude gestures at her.
People muttered about teenage pregnancies.
And Joe, her best friend, had looked at her with such hurt in his eyes
that she had quietly walked from him.
And reality coldly swamped out the golden glory of that baby
struggling to grow within her.

Unmarried, four months pregnant, on her fourteenth birthday, she'd
stood in front of those condemning people with her head held high
and sung from the depths of her soul the most exquisite song of love
for God.
Some laughed and walked away
some were shocked, disgusted
some stayed and revelled in delicious gossip about her
some just sat
but one or two,
like Joe,
were transfixed.
For it seemed for a glorious moment, as if she was showing them a
glimpse of something so free and magnificent, that their worn down
souls were set on fire.

The lorry thundered to a halt.
With grateful thanks Joe helped her down
and the dark night seemed very lonely.
He pulled and pushed and half carried her through the mud-filled
lanes
towards the beckoning lights,
but he knew that for all the fight in her, she was near the end.

She slumped against the wall whilst he knocked.
Glancing down, he saw her face for the first time in the street light
and his heart missed a beat.

The colour had drained,
the eyes had no sparkle or fight left in them.
They were huge and full of pain
and deeply frightened.
He flung his foot in the doorway as the man tried to shut it.
For God's sake, give her a room!
The owner raised his hands in despair, then sighed,
Bottom of the garden, disused air-raid shelter...at least it's dry.

Joseph laid her carefully on the stone floor.
O God, help me, she whispered.
And Joseph held her hand,
told her she was wonderful and he loved her
and that she was a fighter.

And holding onto him
she remembered, dimly, the call and how she had danced,
remembered the pain in her parents' faces as they watched her suffer,
remembered the humiliation that Joseph had gone through.
And in the darkness of that wild night,
she held fast onto his faith
and looking into his eyes
saw the light of God –
and her heart leaped within
and her wearied soul blazed again
as the baby's cry pierced the horror of such a place.

She held the wet bundle in amazement, gently touched the screwed
up little face, as he struggled to breathe,
and suddenly she understood what life with God was all about.
And holding him close, she wept.

As dawn broke the darkness,
the first arrived,
and whispered to the man,
who looked at the woman
who was wild and beautiful,
full of strength and courage and passion.
They want to know his name.

And the untamed girl,
who had travelled far to become the woman of God,
held out her arms
to them in welcome

Emmanuel!

RENDEZVOUS, watercolour

When the world
has dimmed your light in me,
When I can no longer
remember your face,
When I am in despair
and do not know if I will ever find you –

may I journey for a while
upon the faith of others

until the time
when I can know it through my soul –
Emmanuel!

God is with us.
God is with us.

God is with us.

THE PUBLICAN

Been jammed at the door since eleven that morning.
Merry shoppers pushed and jostled,
office parties poured in;
pre-lunch drinks,
lunch drinks,
post-lunch drinks;
drinks to toast the afternoon,
drinks for the road,
pre-dinner drinks;
and finally, serious drinking in earnest.
And the night dropped suddenly.
And the coldness of day was forgotten in a hazy, warm, best buddy
atmosphere.

The publican rolled out the barrels
joking with the men, winking at the women,
letting the beer flow and the tills ring.
But underneath the forced jollity,
his head was pounding, his back was breaking;
tight pains across his chest and down his arms.
Stress, the doctor said.

Stress!
He'd have stress if his wife consistently pushed him beyond the
limit;
if he had a thirteen-year-old daughter who behaved like she was
eighteen;
if he had a so-called chef demanding extra cash in hand;
if he had great louts in his pub,
throwing booze over the walls and grinding cigarettes into the carpet.
Stress!
Tell me about it.

He was in the middle of serving a crowd of leering businessmen,
when his daughter caught his attention.
There's a man at the door wanting a bed. You deal with him.
Exasperated beyond words,
he pushed his way through the tempestuous kitchen,
furiously flung open the door.
A man, a traveller, stood there, clutching a suitcase.
Please. Just one bed.
It was the desperation, the pleading in his face, that was the final straw.

The publican opened his mouth
and all the frustration,
all the tension,
all the hatred,
poured out in a stream of foul and venomous abuse.
The man staggered back,
humiliated,
beaten.
And then the girl stepped into the light
and the publican stopped mid-stream.
Ever so young,
ever so pregnant.
And she looked at him with such clarity,
such compassion.
With a slight smile, she took the man's hand
and they turned back to melt into darkness.

*Hey! You won't find anywhere now. If you're really desperate there's the garage
at the back.*

He showed the way,
swearing as he slipped on overflowing refuse,
pushed the rusty door ajar,
switched on the bare bulb that swung on loose wires.
Barrels and empty crates and dirty bottles
stank the place out
but the look they gave him
and the quiet thank you pierced his heart.

Promising blankets, he went back –
to the flashing neon lights
and the blaring karaoke
and the booze
and the quick money
and the shallowness
that was his life.

It was nearly dawn when he slipped back, the blankets stuffed under
his arm.
The second he pushed the door he knew it was different.

The couple seemed to be alive,
vibrant
with light,
with warmth.
A strange feeling came over him.

Hearing the door, the traveller stood up warily
but the girl beckoned him forward.

Hesitantly, he stepped amongst the chaos
and looked to see why they were smiling.

And there,
wrapped up inside the suitcase,
a tiny baby clutched life.

The hard-bitten publican stood transfixed,
then slowly bent to touch the baby's hand.
The tiny fingers curled around his own
and held tight.
And something forgotten surged through his soul
and flooded the driest places within
and he lifted his head
and laughed with unspeakable joy.

Christ is born! Emmanuel!

Yorkshire farm, Wharfdale, watercolour

Teach me to be open God
that I may learn –
to seek you in the unexpected,
look for you in the unrecognised,
touch you in the different.

But at this moment,
help me to find you
O Lord,
right here,
before me.

THE CALL

The night air was cold with a chill in it that made the boy edge closer to the heat of the fire. He looked longingly down to the foot of the hills where the others were.
He ached to be with them,
to share their comradeship,
to laugh at wicked comments of quick tongues,
to be safe and secure.

He sighed as he thought of those high up on the ridge with him.
The old weather-beaten sheep keeper, his face scarred and furrowed,
eyes now clouding, that had seen all of life,
its snatches of happiness and years of suffering
and hardship
and hand-to-mouth survival.
A silent man whom life had robbed of speech.

As for the third one, the boy was secretly afraid of him.
Glad of his brutal strength when crazed bears prowled
but afraid of the power in his hands –
hands that had once taken a human life.
Afraid of the anger that lay cold and ruthless in him –
afraid of the deadened eyes that saw the weakness of the boy's thin
frame and despised him.

Hard companions for a boy who was young and eager,
excited and foolish,
in the giddy struggle to become a man.
A boy sent to the hills to learn of life.
A boy oppressed by silence and hatred.

He became aware that the old man was standing,
his body breathing with the wind.
Dim eyes turned upward,
searching the dark sky.
The old man knew.
A lifetime of belonging to the elements alerted his whole being.
Something was happening.

The air trembled strangely.
For an awesome moment he knew that
something wilder than anything he had ever encountered was about
to happen.

The air around them splintered with shards of light
as a piercing sound rippled and broke like a wave over the sheep
keepers;
poured through their veins like burning fire,
setting them free to find the wild within themselves,
lit the passion to answer the call.

And then just as suddenly as it came, it was gone.
And the sheep stirred restlessly
but were unafraid
and the wind blew cold in the dark.

The boy moved first.
We have to go. We must answer it.
But the men stared at him silently,
this fragile boy.
But the call of the light blazed within him.
We must go!
he shouted urgently
and pushed them to the path.

The old man struggled to put thoughts into coherent speech
and gave up, following in bewilderment.
But the third one came slowly, reluctantly dragging after them.
For this man of brutal force was an outcast,
banished to be a wanderer amongst the sheep keepers,
away from society.
Sharing in other's food and fire but not their friendship,
for all were afraid of this man of repression and violence.

When the light had flooded through him,
it was as if all the hatred had been pierced,
and in that moment he saw a glimpse of life as it could be.
And everything in him leaped at the chance.
But just as suddenly it had gone.
Reality rushed back.

To his embittered soul, the glorious hope seemed a mockery,
especially when he looked at the boy he despised
and the old man he ignored.

Yet still he came.

They found the cave.
Scrambled over the boulders and edged their way in,
cautious of what they would find.
And were welcomed by an ordinary man, just like them,
and a slip of a girl cradling a tiny babe.

And suddenly all of them were awkward
and uncertain
and overcome.

And then the old man stepped forward and his throat,
silenced by the sights and hardship of life,
struggled and contorted to form words.

We have been called.
We have come to look upon the face of God.

And the young boy wanted to join him but was afraid,
as he was of life,
and his courage faltered.
But then the girl looked up,
and youth called to youth.
Smiling shyly, he knelt beside her and bent his head to her whisper.
And then they were all silent
while the third one fought with his hatred and rage.

And the tired girl saw and beckoning him forward,
laid the tiny gasping baby
into the hands of cruelty.

And the world held its breath,
as power
and fear and violence
and destruction and terror,
gazed upon the weak and defenceless and the trusting.

And the man's fingers curled around that baby,
clutched him to his being.
He bowed his head and rocked and wept.

They didn't go back to the hillside.
They knew their days together were over.

The call still surged through their beings.
Each in his own way had to answer it.

Before they parted, the old man pointed to the low star, touched by
the coldness of a new day.

And the third one smiled at the old,
caught the boy to himself in a tight locking embrace,
and then was gone,
swallowed up by the dark.
They knew they would not see him again,
he would continue to wander
from group to group.
And as he moved
he would spread
the tale of God in a cave.

The boy turned and touched the old man's face in farewell
and then ran leaping away
back to tell his people.
The old man thought of those who would come to his own fire place
and how he would tell them of this night.
And then he stopped
and spinning round,
called out,
Wait! What did she whisper to you?

And in the cold dawn of life
the boy's voice came back,
filled with strength
and joy
and laughter
and his answer reverberated off the grey hills

Emmanuel!

Delight which floods my soul –
As I stand uncertain on the brink of life,
keep me true to all your loveliness.

Christ of my brother's hands –
Hold me fast.

Light which pierced my darkness –
Enable me now
to become the one of strength you seek.

Christ of the broken hands –
Hold me fast.

BRINGING IN THE BOAT, *watercolour*

Christ who surrounds me –
Although my feet slowly tread this earth,
My eyes follow only you
as I move towards my final journey.

Christ of the shepherds' hands,
I beg you –
Hold me fast.

STARGAZERS

It was the old man who first spotted it.
All year it had been most disturbing –
the strange patterns,
the different dances that the great stars were weaving,
auras and lights that had no precedence.

Until one magnificent evening as the light began to fall,
he had stood upon his castle balcony and had seen it with his
naked eye,
a great shining diamond just above the horizon.
And his heart had leaped with a strange mixture of incredulous joy
and terrifying awe.

As his private jet flew to Palestine, he wondered how many of the
others would be there.
Not that he enjoyed their company. In fact, they made him glad he
lived in isolation,
perched on the top of his mountain.
And then suddenly he remembered that star
and his heart leapt strangely again
and his mind dwelt on its meaning.

He'd been there a matter of hours before she arrived.
Her long limousine slowed to an elegant stop.
Her chauffeur bowed low over her door, the crowd gasped and
cameras flashed, as she gracefully unfurled her legs to step into the
bright sunlight.

He had to admit to being rather surprised.
Of them all, he would have thought she would be the last to
understand, she of the Parisian suits and chic hair, shimmering
smoothly in the world of television, surrounded by sparkling
publicity and adoring fans.

And then,
above the razzmatazz,
their eyes met.
And, for a moment, he saw a light in them that no staging could create.
She too had clearly seen the star.

When the other arrived, he couldn't help but sigh. Why did this
young protégé
always engender such despair.
Torn off shorts, worn through trainers, a single glinting earring,
shaved head, except for a ponytail rising ridiculously from the centre
of his bald dome.
But there he was, leaning dangerously out of the train window,
waving vigorously to them both, falling over the platform in his haste.
And the delight of the star was shining out of his face.

They went of course to the palace but to no avail.
King was suave, polished and utterly shallow
and so they slipped away from the court and the crowds,
walked quietly, watching,
always watching the great star that spun before them.

Seedy hotel, run-down, full of rowdy lager louts.
They avoided the glaring lights and the beer and the noise;
made their way round the back,
past dustbins and drunken couples,
and suddenly found what they were looking for.

The startled gaze of a man holding a tired girl,
clutching, in wonder, a tiny babe.

And down in that littered back yard,
the wealthy man slowly knelt
and speechlessly offered his gold.
And in awe,
the woman undid her hair
and let it fall luxuriantly to her feet,
as she simply held out perfume.
And the brilliant young man
crouched at the side of the girl,
with a face translucent with joy,
and with pain,
and offered the child myrrh.

They left as quietly as they had come,
and climbed the hill together,
pausing at the top before they parted company.

They knew their lives had been changed –
for they had answered the sign
and they had looked upon the face of God.
Fleetingly seen something
of the wisdom,
the folly
the power
the vulnerability
the magnificence.

And now they were bound to each other –
hearts on fire.
     God is with us
whispered the wealthy
and in the dark the woman's hand found his.
But the young man looked down upon the crowded city,
then up at the glory of the stars
and with his feet firmly on the ground,
he flung his arms to heaven

Emmanuel!

SUNSHINE ON SNOW, egg tempera

O brilliant star
born from the Creator
to summon those who are waiting,
let me hold within my heart
a minute fraction
of your splintering light –

thus to burn away
the thinning glitter of this world;
thus to love immeasurably
the desperaté of this world;
thus to feel
the sharpness of the joy within this world.

And so become reflections of the Light
that guides the seekers,
whilst ever moving onward,
in the unfolding discovery
of my quest.

WHO AM I?

The town was unbearably suffocating.

The men had come a long way.
The road had been rough.
Like all journeys it had been one of ups and downs.

The man looked at their tired faces
and understood.

Led them away from the heat
and the crowds
and the smells
and the noise
and the flies.
Let them weave their way amongst tall green corn,
climbing steadily and surely
until they reached the top.
And then they dropped,
lay in the shade,
cool air on damp backs.

And somewhere far below, the sounds of the town busied on.
And above them, the leaves whispered in the breeze.

The man studied them.
Who do people say I am?

One of them, by far the liveliest, sat up
and shot a glance at Peter.
Well... John thinks you're Elijah.
        I do not.
That's what you said.
        I did not.

Peter's laugh rumbled around the hillside,
one of those laughs that caught you unawares,
made you want to join in.

He looked at the man, saw he was smiling.

Thomas, the restless, flicked a pebble at a lizard,
I heard them say John the Baptist.
        Nah... most people think you're a prophet.

And above them the breeze rustled the leaves.
And somewhere far below, the sounds of the town busied on.

Peter stirred, watched the man intently.
The man suddenly turned and looked directly at him,
Who do you think I am?

Suddenly alert –
suddenly very still,
noise quiet,
heart booming,
Peter held the gaze.
You are the Christ.

And the man began to talk –
talked deeply of the future,
talked deeply of suffering and of pain,
talked deeply of death,
and deeply of resurrection.

But
the words flowed around Peter like some tumultuous grey sea that
caught him, slapped him, choked him, drowned him.

No!
He leapt up and grabbed the man.
No. This is not true. This is not what we've given up our lives for.
We will not let you suffer.
Like a whiplash the man spun, eyes blazing,
        Get behind me Satan.

Blow of words,
thudded in his stomach,
heaved inside.
Men up on their feet...silent, terrified.

And somewhere far below, the sounds of the town busied on.
And above, the breeze rustled in the leaves.

Peter swayed, slipped to his knees, clutched the hem of the man's robe,
held onto it for life.

And the man saw the terrified, silent men,
saw the pain,
the struggle,
the bewilderment to even begin to understand –
and knelt down on the hard earth,
strong hands lifted the heavy head of the crumpled fisherman.
My friend, why do you weep?

The enormous giant of a man,
the rock in storms, the strength that all looked to,
struggled to put into words
the enormity of feelings that surged through him.
And a terrible cry was dragged from the pit of his being,
a cry that has been echoed in soul after soul –

O God, why does life hold so much suffering?

And the man very gently took the great fisherman in his arms and
cradled him,
understood all their thoughts,
all their fears,
fears of pain,
of uncertain days,
fears of letting go of loved ones,
fears of the unknown.
And at the end –
fears of having to enter the dark abyss of the ultimate journey.

And when he spoke, his voice was very quiet, yet set the air trembling,

I shall lead the way.
Then as you tread, remember I have walked ahead.
And at the very end, there will be no dark abyss,
because I will be there...
and I shall be waiting for you.

And suddenly, the sparkle, and the fire and the power and the passion was uncontainable in the man.

Come Peter, he cried.
I cannot give you an easy life,
but I promise you that this life and the next,
will be with me.

He leapt from that quiet place,
hurtled down the mountain side towards the heat of the city.
Laughing, shouting, leaping.

And something incredible
and wondrous
and frightening
and magnificent
beckoned the men.

Peter lumbered to his feet, and as one, they ran after the man, laughing, crying, calling him to wait.

And the man stopped and turned, and his face was lit with joy, and he flung wide his arms to them.

Wait for me Jesus!

BLAZE OF TREES, pastel

Charisma igniting my dreams
into reality
Power beyond depth holding the
unknown
Tenderness illuminating my soul

Rebel brother
Son of God
Jesu Christus.

You exhaust me, delight me,
terrify me.

Incredible
Wondrous
Frightening
Magnificent.

You make my life worth living.

The Anointing

The light began to drop.
   Cool shadows filled the spaces between the streets;
   houses beckoned with warming glows
and voices dimmed within.

Except for one

where doors were open
so the night air could cool the heat.
And kitchen noises were swallowed by chatter,
that rose and ebbed
into the darkening sky.

She wasn't sure why she had come.
But like the shadows, moved amongst the crowd
until she found the window,
and then gazed upon the men, reclining as they dined.

Twisted round to scrutinise
the one they called
the healer.
Confessed to feeling disappointed
for like the others
he was so ordinary.

But as she turned away the man looked up,
their eyes met
and the gaze was caught.
And suddenly,
life was held,
noise was dimmed,
heart was slowed.

And in that gaze
she wanted to close off her world
and rest with him,
wanted him to know her
in a way that man could not,
wanted to give
but needed him to ask.

And the man watched and waited,
and when she finally allowed,
read her soul,
understood her ugliest
delighted in her purest.

Seeing all
forgave,
filled,
loved.
And his smile welcomed her home.

She turned quickly away
life spinning,
noise roaring
heart pounding.

Pushed the people aside
feet flying down cold streets,
bursting through the door,
jars, bottles
scattered, cascading,
found, clutched
the exquisite perfection.
Back amongst cold streets,
stomach heaving,
icy insides,
burning skin.

Open doorway,
harassed servants,
kitchen heat.
Became them,
rushing through,
pushing aside
shoving,
fighting past.

Men talking
mouths open
robes white,
skin brown.
Night heat,
icy inside,
burning skin,
turmoiled heart
Then stop.

At his feet
looking,
asking,
begging.
And the offer was still there, held in the warmth of his smile
and the love in his eyes.

Her lips formed *thank you* but no words came.
Her breathing caught,
physically wrenching up from the emptiness inside,
welling and growing
until the sound filled the room,
overflowed,
poured out in waves,
shattering,
body breaking,
beyond human bearing,
terrorising the room of men.

And at last
she was released
and her tears coursed down his feet,
as she laid her worn-out soul upon them.

And having gone beyond,
it was as if her whole being,
her whole awareness,
everything that could be awakened within her,
was suddenly,
acutely,
piercingly
made aware of the vastness,
the brilliance,
the source,
the magnificat of all being.

And in that moment
she saw,
sensed,
became open,
to the living and the dying of this man.

And death suddenly swamped the room.
And her heart thudded at the enormity of the task before her.
And in the trembling her fingers slipped
and shot through the fragile glass
and liquid streamed out through her hands
and fell onto his feet.

And the sweetness filled the air
and bathed the room
and touched upon them all.

And the woman gazed at the deep slivers
that slit her hands,
and at the beauty that flowed out,
and looked at the man –
who understood –
and reality came rushing in
and it was over,
it was done.

Gently she drew her hair
around his feet
and wiped them tenderly.
Then kissed them once again in final acclamation.

She straightened up to face the room of silent men
and stepped amongst them,
her eyes not seeing fear or hate
but only God
reflected in the light.

Then at the door she stopped,
and turned,
and looked back one more time
to the man they called
the Christ.

And slowly,
wonderfully,
beautifully,
from the depth of her being
she laughed.

AUTUMN, pastel

Jesus Christ
my gracious friend

I am yours
and you are mine.

Thanks be to God.
Amen.

Chapter Four
EASTER

SET FREE

It was dark when she stirred from a sleepless night.
The taste in her mouth was bitter,
her being unbearably heavy
with the sickness that comes with death.

Waiting for the others, she didn't know how to stand up,
coldness of dawn,
the numbness holding her arms,
stabbing at her heart.
She pushed her shawl away,
trapped by its tightness.

Where lay the truth?
Where was the promise?
Why had everything, *how* had everything gone wrong?
If only he'd stayed in Galilee.
If only they'd not gone to the garden.
If only the men had had their wits about them.
If only...
The nightmare spun on.

She didn't know how it had happened so quickly, so awfully.
And she had done nothing.
Why hadn't she gone out there and fought for him?
Why hadn't she begged them to take her instead?
Why hadn't she broken the taboos
and stood up for him?
Instead, she'd just stood there,
watching,
whilst his broken body slowly died.
She lifted her face to the sky and her leaden soul screamed silently
with despair,
grieving desolation.

She saw the other two, their faces drawn and ill in the greying light;
women who had silently watched the crucifixion –
and in the watching had been crucified,
had silently watched the end
and in the ending had died too.

Cold stones to stumble over,
cold lives to get through.
Twisted, hollow trees,
twisted empty souls.

It was such a dreary light that it took a moment to register the empty
doorway.
They stopped uncertain, terrified of the yawning hole, terrified of the
brutality of the soldiers, terrified of being alone and vulnerable.
But –
no mummified body, no stink of death, just the cold air of a new day.

The mother crumpled, her heart breaking with grief.
Oh God, she wept. *No more. I can bear no more.*
Sobbing uncontrollably,
shattering the in-between silence,
dragging death and grief into the new day.

But Mary stayed and as the light changed, her grieving turned to rage.
I will not cry, she whispered furiously.
I did not fight for him in life but I'll fight for him in death.

Seeing the gardener amongst the broken trees, she ripped the shawl
from her head, strode in seething anger.
You know don't you. Where have they put him?
And the man smiled.
A smile of such life and strength and hope
and unbearable loving,
and her heart turned within her.

> *Mary!*

And the sun tipped over the horizon and flooded that desolate dawn,
setting the stones on fire,
touching the broken,
the jagged,
the twisted
with translucent beauty,
as God burst free on earth.

And her arms reached out

Jesus!

Sussex Winter, watercolour

A. D. ASKEW

Hold me for a moment,
caught into that space in time –
when heaven burst with exultation
as recognition changed our world.

And, hold me just a little longer,
as awesome joy of such
unprecedented force
pours over me,
rollercoasting my emotions.

And hold me, please,
just a fraction more –
so that I can hear again
the voice that speaks
and unbelief is broken.
For quite clearly
I hear not "Mary" but another called.
And my heart races with delight
for the name you call
is
mine.

THE STRANGER

There was no point in looking back.
Three crosses etched against the sky,
brutal, violent, bloody.
Scars in the memory.

The two travellers were wrapped within themselves,
encircled by pain and despair,
so didn't notice the man waiting at the side.
He made them start,
appearing as he did from the quickening shadows.
May I journey with you?
They nodded silently, barely glancing at him.
And so he fell in step with them,
yet it seemed a struggle for him to check his stride to theirs,
so full of life and vitality and exuberance was he.

Conversation was stilted and disjointed,
until in exasperation the bigger of the men stopped and looked at
the stranger.
Look! We don't want to talk.
He put his hand to the side of his head.
We've had it up to here, do you understand?
Leave off will you?

The stranger nodded slowly yet did not withdraw from them.
And they walked on
and the silence seemed heavy.
But it was impossible for him to be silenced and in the end,
he had to ask,

Why do you grieve so much?

The other traveller needed to talk and with a deep breath he turned
to the stranger,
We watched our friend die, he began
and in the dusk he saw again,
in the face of the stranger,
the look of the man he loved
and his grief caught him and his voice broke
and he turned away to smother down the pain.

He was more than our friend, the first traveller rapped out furiously.
More than that.
Bigger, stronger.
He felt the rage growing inside him.
We had such dreams, such hopes, such belief that we could change the world,
feelings and thoughts bigger than words can ever describe.
But as he spoke,
the rage started to erupt into an angry tide within, obscuring sense or
reason.

But he's dead! he shouted at the stranger. *D'you understand?*
Dead and cold and empty, just like our hopes and dreams.
D'you know what it's like to be like that?
To really believe in someone and then he's gone.
And you think he'll walk back in through the door
or it's his voice in the crowd
or he's just round the corner.
And then you remember –
he's dead.
It's finished and nothing's left.

The traveller stopped, dimly aware that he was towering over the stranger,
pushing him back with the force of his rage.
And he felt very cold,
and his eyes were filled with death and his voice was very quiet,
And worse than all the anger, all the hate, all the guilt,
is the pain.
Because at the heart of it, we loved him so very much.

The traveller slowly dropped his hands
and turned back to the road.
You could never understand this hell.

And because the light had dropped
and their hearts were not seeking,
they did not see the look on the face of the stranger
or they would have recognised
one who had lived through hell,
through pain at its most searing,
through human grief at its deepest.

But the light had dropped.
And the moment passed
and the stranger fell back in step with them.

And this time, somehow, it was different.
This time, they all talked –
of the past and the present,
of dying and living,
of God and themselves.

And the journey flew by and they forgot their weary hearts
and Emmaus was before them.

They hesitated at the crossroads, suddenly awkward at parting.
Didn't want to let go.

Come home with us, they said.
And the man whose sorrow was caught with rage,
held out his hand in welcome.
Please! Come home with us.

Simple words,
simply offered,
simply received.

And the house of mourning lit the lamps,
and the families gathered around the table
and watched the stranger with respect.

And the stranger took the bread and blessed it,
and as his strong fingers tore it in two he bowed his head
and it was as if he could no longer bear their lack of seeing,
for when he looked up his eyes shone with the truth
and with arms flung open,
he offered broken bread.

Jesus!

Keep my heart seeking Lord
So I do not miss you
when I pass through the shadows.

Keep my heart seeking Lord
so I do not obscure
your many attempts to talk to me.

Keep my heart seeking Lord
so I may recognise you
in the many forms of broken bread.

Keep my heart seeking Lord
so I can walk the heaven on earth
for you are walking with me.

THE LAST ANGLER, *watercolour*

LIBERATED

The wind lifted the hair of the great fisherman,
    scurried down his damp back
    but he gave no sign of it.
Thomas and Nathaniel exchanged uneasy glances,
their hearts were dancing, glowing with light and love,
Jesus *was* alive!
They'd seen him, touched him, been transformed,
so all this night their hearts were singing,
even though the nets were empty.
But Peter, their immense ox-like leader,
who should have broken the floors with his thunderous dancing,
was still silent,
avoided them,
moved from their world in some tortuous place of his own.
And guilt, the coiled serpent, lay heavy within his stomach.

That other morning, they'd all been so desolate.
Sleepless, aching bodies,
hearts lurching uneasily at the sound of running feet.
But not their leader.
He was unrecognisable,
propped up in a corner of the room,
empty staring eyes,
sickly grey.
When they tried to lift him,
his legs had given way
and his mouth had opened in a terrible, soundless scream.
Afraid, they'd tried to hold him in their arms
but he was barely warm
...and they knew he was going, his soul was dying.

Even when the women returned,
hysterical,
laughing,
crying,
shouting,
the fisherman hadn't moved.
When Mary caught his hands,
infusing her life into the leaden body,
she had met no response
and unable to stay,
she had whirled excitedly on
and not noticed the tears that coursed down his face.

Forked-tongued voices echoed inside Peter's head –
I was there
I was his brother –
should have fought for him,
bargained for him
protected him,
shielded him.
And the worst thought of all,
I should have taken his place.
And the sickness filled him
and he saw himself screaming,
once,
twice,
and yet again,
"I know no Jesus."

Afterwards, he too, like the others, had seen Jesus in the room
and slowly surfacing out of some terrible nightmare,
tried to speak to him,
to reach out to him
but
his limbs didn't move
and then
Jesus was gone.

His mind was in a whirl, heart pounding.
If I could just see him once again I could tell him,
tell him I'm sorry.
If only...
...*O God, just one more time.*

And then,
amazingly,
Christ was among them again.

Smiling at Thomas,
holding out his hands,
laughing at him,
teasing him.

Peter staggered up, tried to reach out,
opened his mouth to call
but the leaden serpent raised his head inside
You fool Peter, he hissed, *you great lumbering coward.*
You're the last man on earth he'd want for a friend.
Your chances are no more.

So when the stranger on the shore told them to throw their nets over,
Peter spun round in the boat.
Tricky light,
hard to distinguish clearly,
cold too,
but there was something,
something that ripped at Peter.
Voice was different,
figure was different but...

As if struck by stars, he plunged into the chopping grey waters,
felt the iciness seize his very heartbeat but couldn't stop,
heard the voices crying out, laughing, fish thudding in the boat
but he was drawing nearer, the sand grating against his legs, the
weight of the water pulling him down, thrashing, falling through the
waves, his voice gasping, crying, shouting with joy,
>   *Jesus........Jesus!*
He was going to sweep him up in his arms,
cradle him,
never let him go
But then he was there.
And Jesus was so much bigger than he'd remembered.

And the great fisherman fell to his knees
and his hands reached out desperately to touch Christ's feet.

And down among the stones,
Christ knelt
and took Peter's great head in his hands.
>   **Simon Peter. Do you love me?**
And deep into Christ's eyes looked Peter.
Dragging his strength together,
he forced out a whisper,
Yes Lord
I do love you.
>   **Then feed my lambs.**

> **Simon Peter do you love me?**
And Peter struggled to breathe,
gasped for air,
Yes Lord, I love you.
> **Then tend my sheep.**

> **Simon Peter. Do you love me?**
And the intensity of Christ shook through the fisherman.

And Peter broke down and wept,
as a cock crow sounded from the hills,
lingered around them a moment
before drifting out to sea.
O Jesus, Jesus, you know I love you.

And Christ read the turmoil in Peter's face
and understood his anguished heart.
He pulled Peter to his feet
and it was as if they were caught in a moment of time.
> **Feed my sheep.**

And as Peter let go of his guilt, he felt an enormous wave of terrible
joy and piercing sorrow break through him, almost as if a cross had
been, momentarily, laid upon him, and staggering he gazed up at
Jesus in wonder and fear.

But Christ smiled and looked at Peter with great love –
and offered his hand.
> **Come Peter.**
> **Follow me!**

Slowly Peter straightened his back
and the joy he'd waited so long for
flooded through him.
His face radiant with light,
the great fisherman's answer rumbled round the earth,
shot to the heavens
and echoed resoundingly back

Hallelujah!

Guilt is such a terrible force O God,
pinning me to an inturned world,
insidiously closing off all touch of life,
shutting me into hell on earth.

Let me then hold tight within my hand
a simple cross,
and feel its roughened wood,
its sharpened corners.
And slowly I will come to find
a greater force –
deeper, stronger, wilder,
freeing us together.
A force that is of you O God.

I am set free.
Now my life begins.
For I begin
with you.

NORFOLK BOATYARD, *watercolour*

Chapter Five

PENTECOST

The Gift PAGE 81

Prayer: Spirit unseen, burn strong within my soul.

PAGE 87

THE GIFT

Jesus had burst back into their lives!

At the memory, Peter's heart jumped –
to be hurtled from the brink of the dying soul
to the incredulous euphoria of reality –
he needed time to let it all sink in.

And, in a way, time was what they'd had.

When Jesus had left them, he'd told them
to wait
and so they waited.

The first few days had been ones of great anticipation.
Overwhelming excitement had filled them,
they felt,
they believed,
that they could do anything.

Bursts of laughter had suddenly rocked them,
everything about them was enormously noisy,
they seemed exuberantly uncontrollable.

And then, as the days passed,
that initial sense of intensity
had worn away
leaving a feeling of flatness.

And gradually, the talk turned to the present
and one by one,
they began to ask out loud,
What do we do now?

Peter drew his attention back to the room.
The practicalities of living were having to be faced.

Is it possible that the Holy Spirit could be here now?
I mean, supposing we didn't understand what Jesus was saying,
supposing we all assumed he meant us to stay here!

Peter sighed again.

It all seemed so clear when Jesus was with them,
he always made one feel able to understand anything.

It was afterwards, when alone,
that life and answers got all muddled up and confused.
He didn't know what to say anymore.

He opened his eyes.
As he'd expected, they were waiting for him to guide them.
And he saw the one of doubt watching him
and suddenly he knew the answer.

What do you think, Thomas?

And Thomas slowly smiled,
Put your trust in Jesus – and have faith.

And the room fell silent.
And it was into this moment of simplicity and profundity, that it fell.

Out of nowhere,
the wind hurled at them with such ferocity
that they were pulled from the floor,
pivoted, spinning –
held upright by some unseen force –
as it whipped around them,
ripping them,
splaying their fingers out,
lashing their hair.

And at the height of his terror,
it came quite clearly to Peter to let go of his fear,
for he was being held.
And gradually,
slowly,
he relaxed –
and found himself leaning into the hurricane –
breathed in its wildness
felt it rush through his body,
through his mind,
clearing it of doubts and fears and worries.

He leant further in,
laughing with delight as the wind
roared at him,
vaguely aware that the others had discovered the joy,
were reaching out and catching hands
caught in the breathtaking
exhilaration of power.

And then it was gone.
And they were left,
numbed by the thunder in their ears,
wildness streaming through their beings,
their eyes shining
with a light that was beyond this world.

And because they had been touched
they saw with the seeing-of-beyond,
the coming of the fire.
Before they had time to fear,
the blazing roared into the room,
lighting the sky outside.

And because they had been filled with wind-light,
they saw where others had forgotten to look.

And into the heart of that roaring they gazed,
and held their breath at the magnificence
of the glory created for them,
marvelled at its richness and its depth.

And by the force unseen
they became one
and the heat seared through them
and the blazing glory
rippled and poured into their blood
and woke the essential infinitesimal
of the complexity of being –
until every sinew and fibre
every molecule and particle
every bone and every hair –
was touched by the glory.

And their bodies became
wondrous and complete and vibrant
in the beauty of creation.

And this time
they saw it go.
Like the wind,
it was set loose
into the world.

And the disciples were left transformed.
Their eyes saw with clarity the extraordinary beauty in the world,
minds that had been bewildered were opened and filled with conviction,
bodies in turmoil from the past were set on fire,
souls that were weary were lit with the passion and the wonder of love.

Peter slowly breathed in again the
wildness of the wind,
felt again the burning that shot through his blood,
knew that soon it would become
a slow deep simmering within,
giving him the power
to find and share and ignite
the Christ-in-others
that he was to seek.

He looked once more at those he loved
and spoke with surprising gentleness,

This is our empowering...
Now we are the people God wants us to be.

And suddenly he heard in the wind
the laughter of Christ,
felt again his touch upon his face,
and the brilliant fire stars within
leaped to find their maker,
and he could wait no more.

My friends, he cried,
the world is waiting.
And with deep faith,
deep joy,
he ran to the open door.

LATE SUMMER CLOUDS, CROMER, pastel

Spirit unseen
burn strong within my soul.

Spirit unseen
let me breathe you deep within.

Spirit unseen
awaken me to realise
that God is at the very heart
of my existence,
so the ordinary happening
is wondrously filled with God-light.

The Truth is,
I am loved.

I am loved.
Amen.

Leprosy Mission contact addresses and telephone numbers

International Office
80 Windmill Road
Brentford
Middlesex TW8 0QH, UK
Phone: 0181 569 7292
Fax: 0181 569 7808
e-mail:friends@tlmint.org
www.leprosymission.org

TLM Trading Ltd. (for orders)
PO Box 212
Peterborough PE2 5GD
Phone: 01733 239252
Fax: 01733 239258
e-mail:tlmtrading@dial.pipex.com

Africa Regional Office
PO Box HG 893
Highlands
Harare, Zimbabwe
Phone: 263 4 733709
Fax: 263 4 721166
e-mail:tlmaroju@icon.co.zw

Australia
PO Box 293
Box Hill
Victoria 3128
Phone: 61 39890 0577
Fax: 61 39890 0550
e-mail:
tlmaust@leprosymission.org.au

Belgium
PO Box 20
Vilvoorde 1800
Phone: 32 22519983
Fax: 32 22519983
email:olm03919@online.be

Canada
75 The Donway West, Suite 1410
North York, Ontario M3C 2E9
Phone: 1 416 4413618
Fax: 1 416 4410203
e-mail:tlm@tlmcanada.org

Denmark
Skindergade 29 A, 1.,
DK - 1159 Copenhagen
Phone: 45 331 18642
Fax: 45 331 18645
e-mail:lepra@post3.tele.dk

England & Wales, Channel Islands and Isle of Man
Goldhay Way, Orton Goldhay
Peterborough PE2 5GZ
Phone: 01733 370505
Fax: 01733 370960
e-mail:post@tlmew.org.uk

Finland
Hakolahdentie 32A4
00200 Helsinki
Phone: 358 9 692 3690
Fax: 358 9 692 4323

France
BP 186
63204 Riom Cedex
Phone/Fax: 33 473 387660

Germany
Küferstrasse 12
73728 Esslingen
Phone: 49 711 353 073
Fax: 49 711 350 8412
e-mail:LEPRA-Mission@t-online.de

Hong Kong
GPO Box 380
Phone: 85 228056362
Fax: 85 228056397
e-mail:tlmhk@netvigator.com

Hungary
Alagi Ter 13
H-1151 Budapest

India Regional Office
CNI Bhavan
16 Pandit Pant Marg
Delhi 110 001
Phone: 91 11 371 6920
Fax: 91 11 371 0803
e-mail:tlmindia@del2.vsnl.net.in

Italy
Via Rismondo 10A
05100 Terni
Phone: 39 7448 11218
e-mail:arpe@seinet.it

Netherlands
Postbus 902
7301 BD Apeldoorn
Phone: 31 55 3558535
Fax: 31 55 3554772
e-mail:
leprazending.nl@inter.nl.net

New Zealand
P O Box 10-227
Auckland
Phone: 64 9 630 2818
Fax: 64 9 630 0784
e-mail:tlmnz@clear.net.nz

Northern Ireland
Leprosy House
44 Ulsterville Avenue
Belfast BT9 7AQ
Phone: 01232 381937
Fax: 01232 381842
e-mail:
106125.167@compuserve.com

Norway
PO Box 2347, Solli
Arbingst. 11
N 0201 Oslo
Phone: 47 2243 8110
Fax: 47 2243 8730
e-mail:bistandn@online.no

Portugal
Casa Adelina
Sítio do Poio
8500 Portimão
Phone: 351 82 471180
Fax: 351 82 471516
e-mail:coaa@mail.telepac.pt

Republic of Ireland
5 St James Terrace
Clonskeagh Road
Dublin 6
Phone/Fax: 353 126 98804
e-mail:
106125.365@compuserve.com

Scotland
89 Barnton Street
Stirling FK8 1HJ
Phone: 01786 449 266
Fax: 01786 449 766
e-mail:lindatodd@compuserve.com

SEA Regional Office
6001 Beach Road
#08-06 Golden Mile Tower,
199589 Singapore
Phone: 65 294 0137
Fax: 65 294 7663
e-mail:pdsamson@tlmsea.com.sg

Southern Africa
Private Bag X06
Lyndhurst 2106, Johannesburg
Phone: 27 11 440 6323
Fax: 27 11 440 6324
e-mail:leprosy@infonet.co.za

Spain
Apartado de Correos, 51.332
CP 28080 Madrid
Phone: 34 91 594 5105
Fax: 34 91 594 5105
e-mail:
mundosolidari@mx3.redestb.es

Sweden
Box 145, S-692 23 Kumla
Phone: 46 19 583790
Fax: 46 19 583741
e-mail:lepra@algonet.se

Switzerland
Chemin de Réchoz 3
CH-1027 Lonay/Vaud
Phone: 41 21 8015081
Fax: 41 21 8031948
e-mail:mecl@bluewin.ch

Zimbabwe
PO Box BE 200
Belvedere, Harare
Phone: 263 4 741817
e-mail:tlmzim@tlmzim.icon.co.zw

ALM International
1 ALM Way
Greenville, S C 29601, USA
Phone: 1 864 271 7040
Fax: 1 864 271 7062
e-mail:amlep@leprosy.org

To find out more about The Leprosy Mission...

You have already helped The Leprosy Mission in its work by buying this book, the profits from which go to fund the work of the Mission around the world. Perhaps you would like to do more? You could buy products from our catalogue, purchase other books, or make a donation to help TLM continue its healing and supportive ministry to those suffering from the effects of the disease.

...just fill in the form and send it to us. We will send you an information pack from which you can choose how you would like to help. The pack includes a copy of our catalogue.

Title .... Initials ....

Surname ....

Address ....

....

....

....

Postcode.............. Country ....

Code: 251

or phone 01733 239252, fax 01733 239258 or email tlmtrading@dial.pipex.com

TLM Trading Limited
P.O. Box 212
Peterborough
PE2 5GD
United Kingdom

Please use your local Leprosy Mission address if you prefer, see page 88.